Contents

This Pokémon Annual belongs to

Name ....

....

I am .... years old

My Pokémon buddy is

....

EGMONT

We bring stories to life

First published in Great Britain in 2020 by Egmont Books UK Ltd
2 Minster Court, 10th floor, London EC3R 7BB
www.egmontbooks.co.uk

Written Emily Stead. Designed by Grant Kempster.

ISBN 978 1 4052 9729 5
70901/003
Printed in Italy

Ash's Quest Continues!

Ash and Pikachu have travelled far and wide across the Alola region, experiencing adventures they could never have dreamed of! With new friendships forged, battles won and a host of rare Pokémon discovered along the way, Ash is closer than ever before to becoming a Pokémon Master!

Turn the pages to read stories of Ash's legendary adventures, complete the puzzles and check out all the Pokémon that Ash and his friends have met on the islands of Alola in the awesome A–Z.

Destiny is calling!

Rotom Reboot

Ash's Rotom Dex is experiencing a rare malfunction! Can you work out which pixelated Pokémon appears on Rotom's scrambled screen each time?

Read the clues or check the Alolan A–Z pages if you get stuck!

1

Clue: Start from scratch with this Alolan Pokémon.

....

2

Clue: A super-sleepy Pokémon that rarely opens its eyes.

....

3

Clue: Swim with this horned Water-type at your peril!

....

4

Clue: A bouncy Pokémon with a scent that's so sweet.

....

5

Clue: A purple Pokémon whose eyes shine like jewels.

....

6

Clue: A feisty Fire-type with flaming fur.

....

7

Clue: The second evolution of a pup-like Pokémon.

....

8

Clue: Lusamine's Pokémon that looks after the Ultra Guardians' base.

....

The answers are on page 69.

Prepare for Battle

Ash is taking on Team Rocket in a battle to the end! Fill in the missing letters in the names of the Pokémon to defeat Jessie and James.

M _ O _ _ H

VS

_ I _ A _ _ U

M _ M _ K Y _

VS

_ N C _ N E R O _ _

S A _ L _ Y _

VS

L _ C _ N R _ C
Dusk Form

_ _ W E A _

VS

M _ _ L T _ _

M _ _ E A _ I E

VS

N A _ A _ A D E _

_ O _ B _ F _ E T

VS

_ O W L _ T

Now check your answers on page 69. For each correct answer give a point to Ash, while Team Rocket earn a point for each incorrect answer. Count up the points and fill in the name of the winner!

Ash vs Team Rocket
WINNER:

The answers are on page 69.

Scavenger Hunt

At dusk, hungry Alolan Rattata rampage through the city streets looking for their next meal! How many Pokémon can you count altogether? Tick the box with the correct number.

21 ☐ **22** ☐ **23** ☐

Now tick the box to show which type of Pokémon Alolan Rattata is.

☐ **Normal**

☐ **Dark-Normal**

☐ **Poison**

The answers are on page 69.

Snowy Search

Lillie's Pokémon, Snowy, evolved from an Alolan Vulpix into a fabulously furry creature. Help Lillie to find Snowy in its evolved form passing only the letters in the Pokémon's name.

START

D
A
O
I
T
E
G
P
E
L
L
N
E
N
R
A
A
L
A
A
N
K
T
S
E
FINISH

The answers are on page 69.

Watery Wonder

When Ash saw the modest Magikarp evolve into a gigantic Gyarados, he could hardly believe his eyes! Work out the correct order of the puzzles pieces to put the Pokémon back together.

A

B

C

D

E

F

1

2

3

4

5

6

The answers are on page 69.

Having a Blast!

In battles together, Kiawe and this Pokémon have a blast! Join the dots to reveal Kiawe's faithful Fire- and Dragon-type buddy.

Kiawe first met his Turtonator while delivering milk from his family's farm.

The answers are on page 69.

15

Show Me the Metal

After stowing away on the boat that brought our heroes home from Poni Island, some strange metal-munching creatures have landed on Melemele Island. What nobody knows is that these Pokémon are Meltan. What mischief will they get up to next?

Over at the Pokémon School, class had begun. Professor Kukui had planned an interesting lesson.

"Today, we'll be studying ***electronics***," the Professor announced. "Sophocles has designed a Pokémon training machine and I want you all to try to build it."

"All the tools you'll need are right here," Sophocles told his classmates.

"Great! I've never done a project like this before," said Mallow. ***"I'm fired up!"*** Kiawe smiled.

"First, we'll study the example to understand how it works," said Professor Kukui.

"Right!" the class all cheered.

As the friends worked together, little did they know that below them in the Ultra Guardians' base, some strange creatures were causing trouble with a capital T . . . ***Meltan!*** They had munched through any metal they could find – from buttons to switches to chair legs.

Clefable chased the greedy critters into the lift, which took them up to the Pokémon School. Ash and his classmates were too busy working to notice the creatures heading towards their next snack – a tool crate full of metal treats!

"Hey, Ash," said Sophocles. "Hand me the box-end wrench, would you?"

"Sure," Ash replied, handing him the first tool he found.

"Nope," sighed Sophocles. "That's an adjustable wrench."

So Lillie went to fetch the tool, along with a hex nut. But when she picked up what she thought was the hex nut she needed, something squishy was attached to it!

"What is that?" gasped Ash.

Everyone wanted to inspect the creature and began prodding and squeezing it. They didn't realise that it was a Pokémon! To defend itself, the Meltan used *Flash Cannon*, releasing a stunning blast of light energy.

"Woah!" everyone cried, as Lillie quickly let go of the creature.

"It can't be a *Pokémon*, can it?" Kiawe exclaimed.

Rotom Dex ran his checks. *"No data! No data!"* he bleeped.

Even Professor Kukui had never seen a Pokémon like this before. What a discovery!

"Look," cried Sophocles, peering into the crate. "There are tons of them in there!"

Lana's Eevee, Sandy, tried to make friends with the Pokémon. When it playfully began to bash the crate, the Meltan launched their powerful move again.

Ash saw the danger and acted fast. *"Pikachu, use Electroweb!"* he cried.

A web of electric beams appeared just in time to protect Sandy from the blast.

"Thank you!" Lana sighed.

"Take care around these creatures!" warned Professor Kukui.

But Kiawe wasn't listening. He went to pet the Meltan, who this time zapped him with a painful ***Thunderbolt!***

"Wow! They can use Electric-type ***and*** Steel-type moves," said Ash.

Just then, Sophocles spotted that the crate was empty. "All our metal tools and nuts and bolts have gone!" he cried.

"Have those little creatures eaten all the metal?" gasped Mallow.

"Maybe they're ***Steel-type?***" wondered Lillie.

Ash had an idea. He laid a wrench in front of the Meltan. "Here," he said. ***"Wanna eat it?"***

The Pokémon hesitated, before beginning their feast!

"Those ***red cords*** look like tails," said Lillie, studying the creatures.

"And those ***black balls*** look like eyes," added Kiawe. "But they float . . . ?"

"Maybe it's ***magnetism?***" Sophocles suggested. He quickly fetched his electromagnet, to conduct a quick experiment. When he flicked the switch, the Pokémon all stuck to the magnet.

"They must be Steel-type!" Lana concluded.

The next moment, Kiawe's Alolan Marowak began to perform a welcome dance for the metal-munching visitors. But the sight of its flaming bones spinning wildly frightened the Meltan away!

Meanwhile, more of the **mysterious Pokémon** had appeared at Team Rocket's base. All the tools and metal that James and Meowth had bought to fix their van had vanished!

"How could they simply *disappear?*" shrieked James.
Next to James's empty crate was a clue – a half-munched metal exhaust pipe.
"Who could have done that?" said Meowth.
Suddenly, from somewhere in the base, came a series of happy squeaks.
"Pokémon!" cried Jessie, red with rage.
Jessie, James and Meowth searched all over the base to try to find the culprits. James heard squeaks from under the desk, but he was too late. The Pokémon had discovered James's chest full of metal bottle-caps and had had a feast.
"My precious collection!" James cried, holding up a half-chewed bottle-cap.
Minutes later, the sound of tiny snores led James to a storage container. He lifted the lid to discover a host of Pokémon, fast asleep inside!

Jessie picked one up, thinking it was a tool. "Did you buy this, James?" she asked.

"*No way!*" said James. He grabbed the Pokémon angrily. "Are you the ones who melted my bottle-caps and ate our tools?" he questioned.

The Meltan replied by sending a blast James's way, which woke the rest of the Pokémon. *Flash Cannon* sure was a powerful move! While Team Rocket were startled, the tiny creatures fled.

Jessie, James, Meowth and Mimikyu chased the Pokémon into the woods.

"*Stop right there!*" Meowth growled. "You're going to pay for messing with our stuff."

Team Rocket had the Pokémon surrounded. It was *time to battle!*

"Mimikyu, use *Shadow Ball,*" Jessie commanded.

Mimikyu tried to launch its move, but all that appeared was a tiny purple orb that wouldn't even damage a Cutiefly!

James tried next with his Mareanie. "Use *Fight Cannon!*" he ordered.

This time, the Team Rocket Pokémon fired blasts of light in the enemy's direction, sending the mini Meltan flying. But the creatures weren't defeated and blasted straight back, causing a huge explosion.

When the smoke cleared, Bewear appeared. The Meltan took one look at the giant fighter and fled again!

"*After them!*" cried Meowth. With no time to waste, Team Rocket hitched a lift with Bewear, who stomped through the forest after the little creatures.

Back at the Pokémon School, the other Meltan had climbed to the top of the bell tower. The classmates followed to see what the Pokémon would do next.

"They can't eat the **school bell**, surely!" said Kiawe, shocked.

But this time the Meltan weren't there for a feed. Instead, each Meltan's head began to spin wildly, letting out a wailing sound.

"Maybe they're resonating?" Professor Kukui suggested.

"Won't they get dizzy?" Lillie wondered.

It soon became clear what the Pokémon were doing . . . they were calling to their friends in the woods – the Meltan that Team Rocket had discovered. When the Meltan in the woods called back, the ones at the Pokémon School headed to meet them.

"There they go," sighed Ash.

"True," said Professor Kukui. "But we've gathered loads of data on the creatures."

"I'm data-filled!" Rotom Dex agreed. Professor Kukui was right. Ash was excited to go home and speak to Professor Oak – he had so much to tell him!

"We might have found something amazing," Ash told Professor Oak as they chatted, that evening. "A new type of Pokémon . . . Rotom's sending the data to you now."

"What's this?" said Samuel Oak, studying the data. "A creature that eats **metal for food** and **sticks to magnets** . . . it can make its **head spin** and launch **Electric-type attacks?**"

"It could be a Steel-type, too," Ash explained.

Professor Oak was proud of Ash and Rotom Dex. "I'm amazed you've collected so much data," he smiled. "This really could be one of the **great discoveries of our time!**"

Ash and Pikachu did a high-five. **"All right!"** Ash cheered.

They were so busy celebrating their breakthrough that no one noticed the lonely Meltan that had lost its friends. Snuggled safely inside Ash's backpack with its new buddy, Rowlet, Ash was set for another discovery some time very soon!

Our heroes have made an incredible discovery – a new Pokémon that can melt metal! Meltan the hex-nut Pokémon may be full of mischief, but could make a great addition to Ash's team. What will happen next? Be sure to join Ash and his friends as their Alolan adventures continue!

How to Draw Meltan

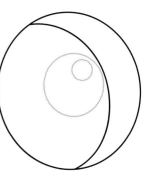

Now that you've met the mysterious Mythical Pokémon, why not try drawing Meltan yourself?

1 Start by drawing a circle with a smaller circle inside it, top right.

2 Draw a larger circle around the bigger circle, then add a line to form a crescent shape.

3 Draw a hexagon shape around the circle, then add some inner lines on the crescent.

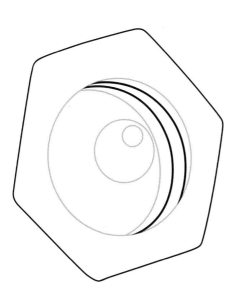

4 Extend the lines at the left side of the hexagon to make it look 3-D.

This tiny Steel-type Pokémon evolves into Melmetal.

5 Draw in the details for Meltan's squishy body.

6 Now draw a cable to form Meltan's tail and colour in this Steel-type Pokémon.

Type Test

This watery word search is ultra hard – only a worthy Ultra Guardian will be able to complete it! Find the names of all 26 Water-type Pokémon hidden in the grid.

R	L	C	W	E	I	M	R	A	T	S	N	P	O	Z	K
D	E	W	P	I	D	E	R	O	L	A	N	T	U	R	N
P	U	P	W	N	N	H	P	H	B	R	I	O	N	N	E
Y	R	P	P	A	V	G	R	T	K	E	U	X	C	K	H
Z	C	I	Q	E	I	N	U	I	O	T	L	A	H	C	S
V	A	J	M	R	P	L	W	L	M	S	C	P	I	U	I
U	T	G	P	A	A	I	O	H	L	Y	O	E	N	D	X
Z	N	Q	A	M	R	T	L	R	T	O	I	X	C	Y	U
W	E	S	L	A	A	I	R	E	D	L	L	E	H	S	R
A	T	K	O	K	Q	G	N	S	P	C	P	V	O	P	B
I	G	C	M	S	U	T	I	A	N	U	P	C	U	P	G
L	Y	U	O	D	A	A	R	K	Y	T	O	N	S	H	F
M	N	D	M	C	N	R	S	R	A	J	P	R	F	Q	W
E	Q	L	O	D	I	V	A	P	O	R	E	O	N	S	N
R	G	O	L	Z	D	T	P	E	L	I	P	P	E	R	Q
R	L	G	A	G	S	D	P	G	Y	A	R	A	D	O	S

POPPLIO
BRIONNE
PRIMARINA
WINGULL
PELIPPER
PSYDUCK
GOLDUCK

MAGIKARP
GYARADOS
TENTACOOL
TENTACRUEL
SHELLDER
CLOYSTER
MAREANIE

TOXAPEX
VAPOREON
DEWPIDER
ARAQUANID
ALOMOMOLA
STARYU
STARMIE

LANTURN
CHINCHOU
BRUXISH
WAILMER
WAILORD

The answers are on page 69.

Alolan A-Z

Travelling through the Alola region, Ash and his friends have met hundreds of Pokémon for the first time, as well as some extraordinary Ultra Beasts. Rotom Dex records all the data for every new creature!

Which Pokémon and amazing Ultra Beasts have you encountered?

Abra

Type: Psychic

Height & Weight: 0.9 m/19.5 kg

Abra is only awake for about six hours a day. Opponents who try to attack during its long sleeping hours will find themselves empty-handed – this Pokémon can teleport out of danger even when unconscious.

Absol

Type: Dark

Height & Weight: 1.2 m/47 kg

Where Absol appears, disaster often follows. Older people tend to blame it for causing these disasters, but many others have come to realise that it shows up early to warn people – and that they should take heed of those warnings.

Aerodactyl

Type: Rock–Flying

Height & Weight: 1.8 m/59 kg

An ancient Pokémon, Aerodactyl has a reputation for ruthlessness and aggression. It was restored from DNA found inside fossilised amber.

Alakazam

Type: Psychic

Height & Weight: 1.5 m/48.0 kg

Alakazam is always learning, and it has an amazing memory. Being able to remember everything it studies leads to this Pokémon's impressive intelligence.

Alomomola

Type: Water

Height & Weight: 1.2 m/31.6 kg

Sailors make sure to have an Alomomola on board during a long journey on the sea so that the crew can stay healthy without stocking up on medicine. This Pokémon is known for taking care of the weak and injured.

Araquanid

Type: Water–Bug

Height & Weight: 1.8 m/82.0 kg

Araquanid uses the large water bubble that surrounds its head to store food and other things it considers particularly valuable. If Araquanid really likes its Trainer, it might try to store them, too!

Arcanine

Type: Fire

Height & Weight: 1.9 m/155.0 kg

Old stories from the eastern parts of the world tell of Arcanine. This Fire-type Pokémon runs with beauty and grace, charming those who see it pass by.

Ariados

Type: Bug–Poison

Height & Weight: 1.1 m/33.5 kg

A nocturnal Pokémon, Ariados spends the day in its web and goes wandering at night in search of food. When it finds something it wants to eat, it wraps the food up with threads spun from its mouth, then chomps.

Beldum

Type: Steel–Psychic

Height & Weight: 0.6 m/95.2 kg

If your office is full of computers, bringing your Beldum to work is a bad idea. When this Pokémon gets irritated, it unleashes a powerful magnetic field that wreaks havoc on any machines in the area.

Bewear

Type:
Normal– Fighting

Height & Weight:
2.1 m/135 kg

With a reputation as the most dangerous Pokémon in Alola, the enormously powerful Bewear poses a huge threat to anyone who gets in its way. If you see it flailing its arms, consider it your cue to back off!

Blacephalon
Ultra Beast

Type: Fire–Ghost

Height & Weight:
1.8 m/13.0 kg

Blacephalon, one of the mysterious Ultra Beasts, has an unexpected method of attack: it makes its own head blow up! Its opponents are so surprised by this that it can take advantage and steal their energy.

Blissey

Type: Normal

Height & Weight:
1.5 m/46.8 kg

Blissey's boundless affection for its Trainer may have played a role in its Evolution from Chansey. It carries an egg that is said to bring happiness to whoever eats it, so some people are willing to pay top dollar for what they consider to be a delicacy.

Bonsly

Type: Rock

Height & Weight:
0.5 m/15.0 kg

Bonsly tries to trick battle opponents into going easy on it by releasing fluid from its eyes as though weeping. Since it needs to control its moisture levels, its 'tears' help it stay healthy – in more ways than one!

Bounsweet

Type: Grass

Height & Weight:
0.3 m/3.2 kg

Bounsweet gives off a sweet, enticing aroma, but it seems to be oblivious to the fact that the smell invites attacks from stronger Pokémon. It tries to scare them off by twirling the sepals on its head, but this doesn't work very often.

Brionne

Type: Water

Height & Weight:
0.6 m/17.5 kg

Seeing an unfamiliar dance gets Brionne excited and eager to learn something new, and it works diligently to do so. It creates water balloons that explode on contact to drive away threats.

Bruxish

Type: Water–Psychic

Height & Weight:
0.9 m/19.0 kg

Bruxish buries itself in the sand at the bottom of the sea and sends out psychic waves to scan the area for food. Attackers are often foiled by this Pokémon's thick skin and powerful teeth.

Butterfree

Type:
Bug–Flying

Height & Weight:
1.1 m/32.0 kg

Butterfree's wings don't get waterlogged if it flies through a rainstorm, thanks to the powder that coats them. The poisonous powder also serves as a deterrent to attackers.

Buzzwole
Ultra Beast

Type: Bug–Fighting

Height & Weight:
2.4 kg/333.6 kg

A strange and mysterious Ultra Beast, Buzzwole has a habit of flaunting its unusually large muscles. It's apparently a common sight on its home world, even though it poses a threat to this one.

Carvanha

Type: Water–Dark

Height & Weight:
0.8 m/20.8 kg

A lone Carvanha is a bit of a wimp, but in numbers, they're terrifying and will spar with Basculin over food. Boaters should take care around this Pokémon, as its powerful jaws can reduce wooden vessels to scrap.

Caterpie

Type: Bug

Height & Weight:
0.3 m/2.9 kg

Caterpie uses scent to defend itself – and it doesn't smell very good! The forked antenna on its head is particularly sensitive, and touching it is sure to provoke a terrible odour.

Celesteela
Ultra Beast

Type:
Steel–Flying

Height & Weight:
9.2 m/999.9 kg

A strange and mysterious Ultra Beast, Celesteela has been spotted emitting massive amounts of energy from its two gigantic arms. It's apparently a common sight on its home world, even though it poses a threat to this one.

Chansey

Type: Normal

Height & Weight:
1.1 m/34.6 kg

The egg in Chansey's pouch is filled with nutrients. Because it's so kind, it won't hesitate to share the egg with a Pokémon who's injured.

Charizard

Type:
Fire–Flying

Height & Weight:
1.7 m/90.5 kg

The flame on the tip of Charizard's tail is a reflection of this Pokémon's fiery power. When Charizard unleashes a blast of fire from its mouth, the flame on its tail burns stronger and brighter.

Charjabug

Type:
Bug–Electric

Height & Weight:
0.5 m/10.5 kg

Charjabug burrows under dead leaves to feast on the rich soil underneath. Its sturdy shell, charged with electricity, protects it from attackers – and from people who step on it by mistake!

Chinchou

Type:
Water–Electric

Height & Weight:
0.5 m/12.0 kg

The lights on Chinchou's antennae can be used for communication – often warning others to stay away from its territory! Trainers who like to go fishing at night find this Pokémon to be a helpful partner.

Clefable

Type:
Fairy

Height & Weight:
1.3 m/40.0 kg

It's unusual to catch a glimpse of this elusive Fairy-type Pokémon. Clefable generally keep to themselves and are fiercely protective of their community.

Clefairy

Type:
Fairy

Height & Weight:
0.6 m/7.5 kg

If you spot a Clefairy, count yourself lucky! These Pokémon aren't often seen, but people just love them because they're so cute and playful.

Cleffa

Type: Fairy

Height & Weight:
0.3 m/3.0 kg

If you go out to watch a meteor shower, be sure to keep an eye on the ground as well as the sky! You might catch a lucky glimpse of a circle of Cleffa dancing in the starlight.

Cloyster

Type:
Water–Ice

Height & Weight:
1.5 m/132.5 kg

Cloyster's shell is harder than diamonds – a quality that helps protect the Pokémon from enemy attacks. It strikes back by launching spikes from its shell.

Comfey

Type: Fairy

Height & Weight:
0.1 m/0.3 kg

Comfey decorates itself with flowers that it picks using the sticky vines on its head. The flowers give off a revitalising scent, and if there aren't any around for it to use, Comfey becomes uncomfortable.

Cosmoem

Type: Psychic

Height & Weight:
0.1 m/999.9 kg

An ancient ruler of Alola referred to Cosmoem as the "cocoon of the stars" and built a shrine in its honour. The golden shell that surrounds its growing body is solid and protective.

Cosmog

Type: Fighting–Ice

Height & Weight:
0.2 m/0.1 kg

Researchers aren't yet sure if Cosmog is of this world, or if it originates somewhere else. It can use teleportation to flee danger, though it doesn't seem to worry about its gaseous body being carried away on the wind.

Crabominable

Type:
Fighting–Ice

Height & Weight:
1.7 m/180.0 kg

A chill wafts from its large pincers as it delivers a hearty pummelling. Apparently, Crabominable can stop an avalanche by standing right in its path and punching as fast as it can.

Crabrawler

Type: Fighting

Height & Weight:
0.6 m/7.0 kg

When two Crabrawler square off, spectators might mistake it for a boxing match – these Pokémon use their big round pincers to punch and block. They climb trees in search of berries, but sometimes they climb Exeggutor by accident.

Crobat

Type: Poison–Flying

Height & Weight:
1.8 m/75.0 kg

Crobat's fangs are so sharp that they cause no pain and leave no mark – so if it bites you at night, you might not know anything happened. This Pokémon has to eat frequently because flying requires so much energy.

Cutiefly

Type: Bug–Fairy

Height & Weight:
0.1 m/0.2 kg

Cutiefly feeds on pollen and nectar, and sometimes it clashes with Butterfree when they both want to snack on the same tasty flowers. It has a knack for detecting the auras of other creatures and plants.

Dartrix

Type: Grass–Flying

Height & Weight:
0.7 m/16.0 kg

Dartrix is very conscious of its appearance and grows defiant if its Trainer doesn't keep it properly groomed. Enemies have a hard time sneaking up on this Pokémon, whose sharp senses easily detect their approach.

Decidueye

Type:
Grass–Ghost

Height & Weight:
1.6 m/36.6 kg

Decidueye pulls the vine attached to its head to narrow its focus so it can take careful aim. It can fire its arrow quills at astonishing speed.

Delibird

Type:
Ice–Flying

Height & Weight:
0.9 m/16.0 kg

Delibird stores food in its tail, and it's happy to share – but occasionally it offers up something that people find unappetising. The bigger a Delibird's tail, the more clout it has in its flock.

Dewpider

Type: Water–Bug

Height & Weight:
0.3 m/4.0 kg

When it ventures on to land, Dewpider brings a water-bubble "helmet" along so it can breathe. If it encounters another of its kind there, the one with the bigger bubble has the right of way.

Dhelmise

Type:
Ghost–Grass

Height & Weight:
3.9 m/210.0 kg

Dhelmise looks like an anchor wrapped in green seaweed. When the seaweed is fully extended, it's hundreds of yards long, so Dhelmise can snare even the biggest Pokémon and wrap them up.

Alolan Diglett

Type:
Ground–Steel

Height & Weight:
0.2 m/1.0 kg

The soil in the Alola region is rich in iron, and the Diglett who live there absorb the iron into their bodies. As a result, three metal whiskers crown Alolan Diglett's round head.

Dragonair

Type:
Dragon

Height & Weight:
4.0 m/16.5 kg

Dragonair doesn't appear often, but when it does, it's apparently a magical sight. One person who was lucky enough to see it reported that it gave off a mysterious aura.

Dragonite

Type:
Dragon–Flying

Height & Weight:
2.2 m/210.0 kg

In the Kanto region, people tell stories about Dragonite, who largely remains an enigma. It apparently lives underwater but can fly through the sky as well.

Drampa

Type:
Normal–Dragon

Height & Weight:
3.0 m/185.0 kg

Drampa loves taking care of children, and it's been known to destroy the homes of people who pick on its favourite kids. So don't be a bully … just in case.

Dratini

Type: Dragon

Height & Weight:
1.8 m/3.3 kg

Dratini is so elusive, people weren't even sure of its existence until fairly recently. The mystery was resolved when a fisherman reeled one in.

Drifblim

Type: Ghost–Flying

Height & Weight:
1.2 m/15.0 kg

When Drifblim's round body starts losing air pressure, it goes in search of spirits to refill itself. There are scary stories about people trying to catch this Pokémon as it goes floating by in the twilight, only to find themselves whisked away instead.

Drifloon

Type:
Ghost–Flying

Height & Weight:
0.4 m/1.2 kg

Many spirits fill up Drifloon's floating body. When someone takes hold of this Pokémon's dangling strings, they often disappear – and Drifloon's body gets bigger. Perhaps there's a connection…

Drowzee

Type: Psychic

Height & Weight:
1.0 m/32.4 kg

Drowzee eats dreams, and apparently it can remember and share what it's consumed. If you sleep next to one, you might find yourself in a dream that used to belong to someone else!

Alolan Dugtrio

Type: Ground–Steel

Height & Weight:
0.7 m/66.6 kg

Each of the triplets that make up a single Alolan Dugtrio wears its whiskers in a different style. This is the result of slight differences in the metal absorbed by their bodies.

Eevee

Type:
Normal

Height & Weight:
0.3 m/6.5 kg

Because it can evolve into so many different Pokémon, researchers believe that Eevee's genes could help them figure out exactly how Pokémon Evolution works.

Electabuzz

Type: Electric

Height & Weight:
1.1 m/30.0 kg

When the power goes out in a large area, it's pretty safe to blame Electabuzz. These Pokémon are known for invading power plants to devour the electricity.

Electivire

Type: Electric

Height & Weight:
1.1 m/138.6 kg

Electivire boasts enough electrical energy in its body to power an entire city for a whole year. It attacks by grasping its voltage-filled tail in its fist, then unleashing punches filled with electricity.

Elekid

Type: Electric

Height & Weight:
0.6 m/23.5 kg

When Elekid's body is fully charged with electricity, its horns turn a bluish white colour, and anyone who touches it receives a shock. It's easy to cheer up when it's in a funk – it perks up when it hears thunder, even just in recordings.

Espeon

Type: Psychic

Height & Weight:
0.9 m/26.5 kg

When Espeon lounges in a sunbeam, it's not just being lazy – it's storing up power in the orb on its forehead. Apparently, a need for self-defence awakened its psychic powers.

Alolan Exeggutor

Type:
Grass–Dragon

Height & Weight:
10.9 m/415.6 kg

Alolan Exeggutor has evolved to its full potential thanks to the powerful energy emitted by the sun over Alola. The strong rays awaken the Pokémon's hidden power.

Flareon

Type:
Fire

Height & Weight:
0.9 m/25.0 kg

When Flareon takes a deep breath, you may want to stand clear! Thanks to a furnace-like chamber inside its body, it's able to exhale flames that exceed 800 degrees Celsius.

Fomantis

Type: Grass

Height & Weight:
0.3 m/1.5 kg

Fomantis begins sunbathing at dawn, spreading its four leaves to absorb light. The top of its head smells nice, and if it gets plenty of its beloved sunshine, its body becomes more colourful.

Garbodor

Type: Poison

Height & Weight:
1.9 m/107.3 kg

Garbodor who live in the Alola region have a reputation for being the strongest, apparently because they're always sparring with rival Muk. Their favourite battle strategy is to imprison an opponent with one arm while spraying a paralysing liquid.

Gastly

Type:
Ghost–Poison

Height & Weight:
1.3 m/0.1 kg

Because Gastly takes the form of a gas, it doesn't have a true shape. It's often found hanging out in abandoned, run-down buildings.

Gengar

Type:
Ghost–Poison

Height & Weight:
1.5 m/40.5 kg

If you suddenly feel the temperature drop, you might want to watch your back. There could be a Gengar nearby, trying to play mean tricks on you.

Alolan Geodude

Type:
Rock–Ground

Height & Weight:
0.4 m/20.3 kg

It's a good idea to keep an eye out when hiking and avoid any rocks you see buried in the trail. Alolan Geodude respond with a nasty shock when someone steps on them.

Glaceon

Type: Ice

Height & Weight:
0.8 m/25.9 kg

When Glaceon chills its body below subzero, the water vapour in the air around it turns to hail, which it pelts at opponents. It freezes its fur into needles to defend itself from attacks.

Golbat

Type:
Poison–Flying

Height & Weight:
1.6 m/55.0 kg

Golbat uses the element of surprise to sneak up on opponents. When they least expect it, Golbat strikes, sinking its fangs into them.

Goldeen

Type: Water

Height & Weight:
0.6 m/15.0 kg

It's quite a sight to see schools of Goldeen heading towards their home waters. Their instincts are so strong that they think nothing of swimming upstream, even up waterfalls, to reach their nests.

Golduck

Type: Water

Height & Weight:
1.7 m/76.6 kg

When it evolves, Golduck becomes much better adapted for swimming, with webbed flippers on all of its limbs. It propels itself gracefully through the lake where it lives.

Alolan Golem

Type: Rock–Electric

Height & Weight:
1.7 m/316.0 kg

Alolan Golem uses the power of magnetism to shoot electrically charged rocks at its opponent. It doesn't worry too much about accuracy, because the rocks give off an electric blast when they land.

Golisopod

Type: Bug–Water

Height & Weight:
2.0 m/108.0 kg

With a diamond-hard shell and sharp claws that it can pull in or reveal as needed, Golisopod is a fearsome force in battle. The skittish Wimpod sometimes travel alongside this much larger Pokémon.

Goodra

Type: Dragon

Height & Weight:
2.0 m/150.5 kg

Goodra's slippery skin and blubbery body let it deflect enemy attacks with ease. It loves being around people, and it shows affection for its favourite ones by embracing them in a sticky hug – don't mind the slime!

Alolan Graveler

Type:
Rock–Electric

Height & Weight:
1.0 m/110.0 kg

Like their Kanto counterparts, Alolan Graveler often travel by letting gravity do the work and rolling down the side of the mountain. Unlike their Kanto counterparts, they can unleash an electric pulse as they roll.

Alolan Grimer

Type:
Poison–Dark

Height & Weight:
0.7 m/42.0 kg

Alolan Grimer loves to eat garbage, and it has a fast metabolism that breaks down meals in no time. Its body is dotted with glittering crystals formed by leftover toxins.

Growlithe

Type:
Fire

Height & Weight:
0.7 m/19.0 kg

Growlithe generally has a friendly disposition, but if it thinks you're an intruder on its turf, it will unleash a frenzy of furious barking.

Grubbin

Type: Bug

Height & Weight:
0.4 m/4.4 kg

Keep your hands out of Grubbin's nest! Its jaws are sharp and strong, and it's likely to nip at any intruder. In battle, it uses its jaws to pin opponents after immobilising them with sticky string.

Gumshoos

Type: Normal

Height & Weight:
0.7 m/14.2 kg

These Pokémon aren't native to Alola – they were imported from elsewhere long ago to control a massive outbreak of Rattata. Gumshoos is known for patience and self-control as it waits for the perfect moment to strike.

Guzzlord

Ultra Beast

Type:
Dark–Dragon

Height & Weight:
5.5 m/888.0 kg

A strange and mysterious Ultra Beast, Guzzlord seems to have an insatiable appetite – it's always eating. It's apparently a common sight on its home world, even though it poses a threat to this one.

Gyarados

Type: Water–Flying

Height & Weight:
6.5 m/235.0 kg

Bearing little resemblance to the weakling from which it evolved, Gyarados has an incredibly destructive temperament and the power to unleash it. This Pokémon was responsible for destroying entire cities in times past.

Hakamo-o

Type:
Dragon–Fighting

Height & Weight:
1.2 m/47.0 kg

Smacking its scales together, Hakamo-o clangs out a rhythm that gets it pumped up for battle. It regularly sheds the metallic scales, which can be collected and used to make cookware.

Haunter

Type:
Ghost–Poison

Height & Weight:
1.6 m/0.1 kg

Don't be fooled by Haunter and its big grin – there's danger inside that mouth! Its licks cause its opponents to tremble uncontrollably, and Haunter takes the opportunity to drain their energy.

Herdier

Type: Normal

Height & Weight:
0.9 m/14.7 kg

As Herdier's black fur grows longer, it becomes stronger and more effective as a shield against enemy bites and scratches. Ancient cave paintings show that this Pokémon species has been living among people for a long time.

Hypno

Type:
Bug–Poison

Height & Weight:
1.6 m/75.6 kg

Hypno mesmerises its foes using the pendulum it carries. If you look into its eyes, you risk being put under its spell.

Igglybuff

Type:
Normal–Fairy

Height & Weight:
0.3 m/1.0 kg

Trainers who don't like noise would do well to steer clear of Igglybuff – they practise their singing all the time, and it's hard to get them to stop even for their own good.

Incineroar

Type: Fire–Dark

Height & Weight:
1.8 m/83.0 kg

Because of its arrogance, Incineroar soon gets bored with a string of easy victories and seeks out tougher opponents to battle. When it gets fired up, that's not just a saying – its belt of flame gives off intense heat!

Jangmo-o

Type: Dragon

Height & Weight:
0.6 m/29.7 kg

Jangmo-o strikes its head scales against hard surfaces to make a loud noise that can scare off attackers or summon allies. Warriors of long ago admired this small Pokémon for its valour.

Jigglypuff

Type: Normal–Fairy

Height & Weight:
0.5 m/5.5 kg

If you have a busy day ahead, avoid looking deep into Jigglypuff's pretty, round eyes. You could end up so mesmerised, you won't even notice when it starts singing a lullaby to put you to sleep.

Jolteon

Type: Electric

Height & Weight:
0.8 m/24.5 kg

Jolteon's mood shifts as fast as lightning – one moment it's joyous, the next it's furious. These shifting emotions somehow increase its electrical charge.

Kadabra

Type: Psychic

Height & Weight:
1.3 m/56.5 kg

Kadabra's presence tends to cause strange things to happen. The hands of clocks sometimes spin in reverse when this Psychic-type Pokémon is around.

Kangaskhan

Type: Normal

Height & Weight:
2.2 m/80.0 kg

Kangaskhan is fiercely protective of the little one who lives in the pouch on its belly. It won't back down from a fight, even one it can't win, if it thinks the little one is in danger.

Kartana

Ultra Beast

Type: Grass–Steel

Height & Weight:
0.3 m/0.1 kg

A strange and mysterious Ultra Beast, Kartana has a body that's as thin as paper but as sharp as a blade. It's apparently a common sight in its home world, even though it poses a threat to this one.

Komala

Type: Normal

Height & Weight:
0.4 m/19.9 kg

If you've ever slept really late on a weekend, your parents might have accused you of sleeping your life away. That's exactly how Komala lives. It even eats in its sleep, munching on leaves that keep it from waking.

Kommo-o

Type: Dragon–Fighting

Height & Weight:
1.6 m/78.2 kg

Kommo-o's scaly fists can deliver crushing blows in battle, and the scales provide protection so it doesn't hurt itself when striking. A shriek of victory often sets off a cacophony of celebration from its companions.

Krokorok

Type: Ground–Dark

Height & Weight:
1.0 m/33.4 kg

Krokorok can't stand being cold, so it burrows deep into the sand to insulate itself from chilly desert nights. If it has to stay underground for a long time, it can eat the food it previously buried as emergency rations.

Krookodile

Type: Ground–Dark

Height & Weight:
1.5 m/96.3 kg

Krookodile takes advantage of the sandstorms stirred up by Flygon, and it hides in the chaos until it spots food – even from miles away. It effortlessly burrows through the desert, using the sand as cover until the time is right for it to leap out and attack.

Lanturn

Type: Water–Electric

Height & Weight:
1.2 m/22.5 kg

Wild Lanturn live deep in the ocean, where sunlight has a hard time reaching them. The light on their antennae, powered by bacteria, flashes brightly to daze an opponent.

Leafeon

Type: Grass

Height & Weight:
1.0 m/25.5 kg

A peaceful Pokémon, Leafeon avoids confrontation – unless its friends are threatened, in which case it attacks with the sharp edges of its leaflike tail. It lives in pristine forests and draws energy from the sun using photosynthesis.

Ledian

Type: Bug–Flying

Height & Weight:
1.4 m/35.6 kg

The spot pattern that covers Ledian's back is thought to have some connection to the constellations – particularly because it likes to fly at night. Some people believe that the sparkling dust it sprinkles as it flies can bring good luck.

Ledyba

Type: Bug–Flying

Height & Weight:
1.0 m/10.8 kg

Ledyba are timid Pokémon who prefer to stick together, using Reflect to shield their nest from intruders. They dislike the cold, so they're quite at home in the tropical warmth of Alola.

Lillipup

Type: Normal

Height & Weight:
0.4 m/4.1 kg

With its agreeable temperament and quick mind, Lillipup is an ideal Pokémon for beginner Trainers. It recognises when it can't win a battle and retreats accordingly.

Litten

Type: Fire

Height & Weight:
0.4 m/4.3 kg

Litten has a dramatic method of shedding: twice a year, it sets itself on fire, and the old fur burns away to reveal a glossy new coat. This Pokémon does best with a Trainer who's willing to give it space.

Lucario

Type: Fighting–Steel

Height & Weight:
1.2 m/54.0 kg

A strong yet sensitive Pokémon, Lucario becomes anxious when it reads the auras of people and Pokémon and detects unpleasant feelings. It can hone its own aura into offensive waves powerful enough to pulverise huge rocks.

Lunala

Type: Psychic–Ghost

Height & Weight:
4.0 m/120.0 kg

An ancient legend refers to this Pokémon as "the beast that calls the moon." When Lunala opens an Ultra Wormhole, it sometimes summons strange life-forms from another world.

Lurantis

Type: Grass

Height & Weight:
0.9 m/18.5 kg

Although its admirers know it as an extraordinarily beautiful Grass-type Pokémon, Lurantis acts like a Bug-type Pokémon in order to fool its foes. It attacks with dance-like movements, slashing away with the sharp petals on its arms.

Lycanroc (Midday Form)

Type: Rock

Height & Weight:
0.8 m/25.0 kg

The rocks sticking out of Lycanroc's mane are sharper than blades, and some people consider it good luck to carry broken-off shards they've found. This Pokémon attacks opponents to wear them down before it deals the finishing blow.

Lycanroc (Dusk Form)

Type: Rock

Height & Weight:
0.8 m/25.0 kg

Lycanroc's Dusk Form is a rare sight in Alola. It only appears when a Rockruff evolves at sunset, during the time between day and night. This Pokémon's calm demeanour hides a strong impulse to battle.

Lycanroc (Midnight Form)

Type: Rock

Height & Weight:
1.1 m/25.0 kg

A solitary Pokémon, Lycanroc will only obey a Trainer who can help it reach its full potential – and even then, it will disregard any command it dislikes. It has no hesitation about being reckless in battle if it knows it can win.

Machamp

Type: Fighting

Height & Weight:
1.6 m/130.0 kg

Machamp bombards its opponents with a volley of breathtaking punches. It's said that each arm has enough strength to move a mountain, so all four together make quite the show of force.

Machoke

Type: Fighting

Height & Weight: 1.5 m/70.5 kg

Inside Machoke is the potential for immense, unyielding power. But for some reason, its true strength is restrained by the belt wrapped around its waist.

Machop

Type: Fighting

Height & Weight: 0.8 m/19.5 kg

Machop may be small in stature, but it's actually quite strong. Because it has practised lots of different fighting styles, it can hold its own in battle.

Magearna

Type: Steel–Fairy

Height & Weight: 1.0 m/80.5 kg

According to myth, a scientist built Magearna many centuries ago, crafting a mechanical body to house the Soul-Heart. This Pokémon has a strong understanding of human emotions and takes good care of anyone who is important to it.

Magikarp

Type: Water

Height & Weight: 0.9 m/10.0 kg

Magikarp live just about anywhere there's water, whether it's salty, fresh, brackish, or just left over from a storm. They're notorious for their lack of reliability.

Magnemite

Type: Electric–Steel

Height & Weight: 0.3 m/6.0 kg

Magnemite gives off strong electromagnetic waves as it levitates through the air. Its movements don't seem to be affected by the force of gravity.

Magneton

Type: Electric–Steel

Height & Weight: 1.0 m/60.0 kg

If you feel your surroundings suddenly become a bit warmer, there may be a Magneton nearby. As it emits bizarre radio waves, the air around it rises in temperature by a few degrees.

Magnezone

Type: Electric–Steel

Height & Weight: 1.2 m/180.0 kg

As it patrols its territory, Magnezone uses radar to detect the movements of opponents, then attacks with a powerful beam. Some people think this Pokémon, which gives off strong magnetic waves, originated in outer space.

Mankey

Type: Fighting

Height & Weight: 0.5 m/28.0 kg

It's pretty easy to make a Mankey mad, and it tends to lash out recklessly at the source of its anger. Give it a wide berth if you're walking through the trees where it lives.

Mareanie

Type: Poison–Water

Height & Weight: 0.4 m/8.0 kg

If Mareanie's body is damaged, it can regenerate overnight if it gets enough rest. It likes to munch on the coral branches that Corsola sheds, which limits the supply available to crafters.

Alolan Marowak

Type: Fire–Ghost

Height & Weight: 1.0 m/34.0 kg

Alolan Marowak can often be seen dancing under the moonlight. The fiery dance is performed in memory of its companions who are no longer around.

Marshadow

Type: Fighting–Ghost

Height & Weight: 0.7 m/22.2 kg

After slipping into the shadows of people and Pokémon, Marshadow is able to understand their feelings and imitate their movements. If it hones its skills enough, it might even surpass them in power.

Meltan

Type: Steel

Height & Weight: 0.2 m/8.0 kg

Meltan's body is made of molten steel. When it finds bits of metal buried in the subsoil, it melts them down and amalgamates the elements into its body.

Alolan Meowth

Type: Dark

Height & Weight:
0.4 m/4.2 kg

Alolan Meowth is known for being proud, crafty, and extremely intelligent. It has a reputation for being a difficult Pokémon to train – but many Trainers seem to enjoy the challenge, because it's also very popular!

Metagross

Type:
Steel–Psychic

Height & Weight:
1.6 m/550.0 kg

Metagross is intimidating both physically and mentally – it can easily pin a foe with its four strong legs, and it uses complicated calculations to analyse its opponents and put them at a disadvantage.

Metang

Type:
Steel–Psychic

Height & Weight:
1.2 m/202.5 kg

Metang's two brains wield impressive psychic power, which it unleashes in battle to trap opponents and stop them from moving until it can grasp them with its sharp claws.

Metapod

Type: Bug

Height & Weight:
0.7 m/9.9 kg

Metapod relies on its shell for protection, and it can make the shell harder at will if it's threatened. No matter how hard the shell is, a massive impact can cause it to pop open.

Mimikyu

Type:
Ghost–Fairy

Height & Weight:
0.2 m/0.7 kg

You don't want to know what Mimikyu really looks like – and it doesn't want you to know, either. Its appearance is rumoured to strike terror into the bravest heart, and it attacks anyone who tries to peek.

Minior (Meteor Form)

Type:
Rock–Flying

Height & Weight:
0.3 m/40.0 kg

Minior lives high in the atmosphere, where it is sometimes pursued by bigger foes. Escape often involves plummeting to the ground. Its hard outer shell is broken to bits in the impact, but the delicate core survives.

Minior (Red Core)

Type: Rock–Flying

Height & Weight:
0.3 m/0.3 kg

When Minior's hard shell cracks and falls away, its colourful core is exposed. Alola is one of the few places to watch a Minior shower, when these Pokémon fall from the sky and show off their many brilliant colours.

Misdreavus

Type: Ghost

Height & Weight:
0.7 m/1.0 kg

Misdreavus gets its energy from scaring people and soaking up their fear, so it's not fond of people who don't scare easily. Each orb of its red "necklace" is full of screams.

Mismagius

Type: Ghost

Height & Weight:
0.9 m/4.4 kg

The incantations that Mismagius mutters under its breath have a variety of effects. Most are curses, intended to give the target a terrible headache or a vision of terror. But once in a while, it will cast a helpful spell.

Morelull

Type:
Grass–Fairy

Height & Weight:
0.2 m/1.5 kg

After nightfall, tourists flock to Morelull's damp forest home, hoping for a glimpse of its glowing mushroom caps. The caps are filled with luminescent spores that fall to the ground around Morelull.

Mudbray

Type: Ground

Height & Weight:
1.0 m/110.0 kg

Mudbray just loves to get dirty! Daily mud baths are an important part of its routine, and missing one can cause distress. This Pokémon can carry a mighty weight on its back with little effort.

Mudsdale

Type:
Ground

Height & Weight:
2.5 m/920.0 kg

Mudsdale boasts impressive stamina and strength. It can haul a 10-ton load through the mountains for days on end without stopping for rest or showing any break in its calm demeanour.

Alolan Muk

Type: Poison–Dark

Height & Weight: 1.0 m/52.0 kg

Muk's favourite food is garbage. In the Alola region, its colouring becomes brighter and more colourful as it consumes more and more waste.

Munchlax

Type: Normal

Height & Weight: 0.6 m/105.0 kg

Munchlax gulps down anything that resembles food – and whatever it doesn't eat, it stashes away in its long fur for a later snack. If it loses track of what it's collected, it'll start to smell bad, but it doesn't mind – it can stomach spoiled food with no trouble.

Naganadel
Ultra Beast

Type: Poison–Dragon

Height & Weight: 3.6 m/150.0 kg

Naganadel, one of the mysterious Ultra Beasts, stores a poisonous liquid in vast quantities inside its body. The poison, which gives off an eerie glow and adheres to anything it touches, can be fired from its needles.

Necrozma

Type: Psychic

Height & Weight: 2.4 m/230.0 kg

Legends say Necrozma came to the Alola region from another world – possibly seeking more light, which it devours to use as energy. If it doesn't get enough light, its body turns dark and still.

Nihilego
Ultra Beast

Type: Rock–Poison

Height & Weight: 1.2 m/55.5 kg

A strange Ultra Beast that appeared from an Ultra Wormhole, Nihilego behaves like it's a parasite of both people and Pokémon. It attacks with a substance believed to be a potent poison.

Alolan Ninetales

Type: Ice–Fairy

Height & Weight: 1.1 m/19.9 kg

Because Alolan Ninetales lives high in the mountains where the snow never melts, people have developed a deep reverence for this elusive Pokémon. Blizzards surround it wherever it goes.

Nosepass

Type: Rock

Height & Weight: 1.0 m/97.0 kg

For the most part, Nosepass stays completely still, but it can quickly drill an escape route through the ground if it's threatened. It uses magnetic power to pull in food, but sometimes it inadvertently reels in a battle opponent instead.

Oranguru

Type: Normal–Psychic

Height & Weight: 1.5 m/76.0 kg

A tree dweller, Oranguru spends much of its time in peaceful meditation – but if it encounters another Oranguru, a battle over intellectual superiority will ensue. It has a tendency to imitate the behaviours of Pokémon Trainers.

Oricorio (Baile Style)

Type: Fire–Flying

Height & Weight: 0.6 m/3.4 kg

After sipping red nectar, Oricorio becomes filled with passion – both for dancing and for battling. It distracts foes with its rhythmic movements, then attacks with fire. It has little patience for incompetent Trainers.

Oricorio (Pa'u Style)

Type: Psychic–Flying

Height & Weight: 0.6 m/3.4 kg

After sipping pink nectar, Oricorio becomes preoccupied with dancing – so much so that it sometimes forgets to acknowledge its Trainer. It uses beautiful movements to relax its opponents, then takes the chance to strike them with psychic attacks.

Oricorio (Pom-Pom Style)

Type: Electric–Flying

Height & Weight: 0.6 m/3.4 kg

After sipping yellow nectar, Oricorio shares its cheer with others by dancing. When its foes are sufficiently distracted, it takes the opportunity to zap them with electricity.

Oricorio (Sensu Style)

Type: Grass–Flying

Height & Weight: 0.6 m/3.4 kg

After sipping purple nectar, Oricorio shows off sophisticated movements that serve as inspiration for other dancers. Its opponents are often impressed, as well – but if they don't pay attention, Oricorio might get the best of them with a curse!

Palossand

Type:
Ghost–Ground

Height & Weight:
1.3 m/250.0 kg

Palossand creates howling sandstorms to prevent its opponents from getting away and then steals their life force. Each grain of sand that makes up this Pokémon's body has a mind of its own.

Paras

Type:
Bug–Grass

Height & Weight:
0.3 m/5.4 kg

Paras gets sustenance by chewing on tree roots it finds underground. Although it does all the digging work, the two mushrooms on its back use up most of the consumed nutrients.

Parasect

Type: Bug–Grass

Height & Weight:
1.0 m/29.5 kg

Parasect is apparently controlled by the big mushroom on its back. By absorbing the energy that Parasect takes in, the mushroom is able to function as the Pokémon's brain.

Passimian

Type: Fighting

Height & Weight:
2.0 m/82.8 kg

Berries serve as both food and weapons for Passimian. They also help determine troop hierarchy – the Passimian who can throw a berry the farthest is the boss. Troops identify themselves by using saliva to attach leaves to their shoulders in distinct patterns.

Pelipper

Type:
Water–Flying

Height & Weight:
1.2 m/28.0 kg

Pelipper's massive beak lets it scoop up huge amounts of food, which it then swallows all at once. Sometimes it totes around smaller Pokémon in its beak.

Alolan Persian

Type:
Dark

Height & Weight:
1.1 m/33.0 kg

Many Trainers seek out Alolan Persian for its beautiful coat of silky fur. When it's moving quickly in battle, the fur ripples in lovely waves as it pounces.

Pheromosa

Ultra Beast

Type:
Bug–Fighting

Height & Weight:
1.8 m/25.0 kg

A strange and mysterious Ultra Beast, Pheromosa has impressive strength despite its dainty body. It's apparently a common sight on its home world, even though it poses a threat to this one.

Pikipek

Type:
Normal–Flying

Height & Weight:
0.3 m/1.2 kg

Little Pikipek has impressive muscles in its neck that allow it to unleash 16 pecks per second to drill into a tree. Its pecking rhythm varies based on how it's feeling.

Poipole

Ultra Beast

Type: Poison

Height & Weight:
0.6 m/1.8 kg

Poipole, one of the mysterious Ultra Beasts, is crowned with needles that spray a dangerous poison. This creature lives in another world, where it is popular enough that it could be a first partner.

Politoed

Type: Water

Height & Weight:
1.1 m/33.9 kg

Be wary of challenging a Politoed whose single hair is extra long and curly – that's the sign of a great leader, and it might unleash an army of Poliwag and Poliwhirl with a screeching cry.

Poliwag

Type:
Water

Height & Weight:
0.6 m/12.4 kg

Poliwag in different parts of the world have belly spirals that curl in different directions. It's much more comfortable in the water than on land.

Poliwhirl

Type:
Water

Height & Weight:
1.0 m/20.0 kg

When Poliwhirl is threatened by an opponent, the spiral on its belly seems to twirl in a mesmerising pattern. Once the foe falls asleep, Poliwhirl makes a quick getaway.

Poliwrath

Type:
Water–Fighting

Height & Weight:
1.3 m/54.0 kg

Even some of the world's best swimmers would be hard-pressed to keep up with Poliwrath in a race. Its impressive muscles move it powerfully through the water.

Popplio

Type: Water

Height & Weight:
0.4 m/7.5 kg

Popplio blows water balloons from its nose, and it practises every day to make them bigger and better. The balloons have a bouncy, elastic surface, and Popplio can make impressive high jumps by climbing on top of them.

Primarina

Type:
Water–Fairy

Height & Weight:
1.8 m/44.0 kg

When the moon is bright, Primarina lifts its beautiful voice, and the rest of its colony joins the song. Watching this Pokémon battle is like watching a ballet.

Primeape

Type:
Fighting

Height & Weight:
1.0 m/32.0 kg

There are rumours that Primeape sometimes chills out and calms down … but since it's always angry when anyone else is around, those rumours are hard to verify.

Probopass

Type:
Rock–Steel

Height & Weight:
1.4 m/340.0 kg

Probopass sends out its three small Mini-Noses when engaging opponents in battle. Sometimes the Mini-Noses stray too far and have trouble finding their way back.

Psyduck

Type:
Water

Height & Weight:
0.8 m/19.6 kg

Poor Psyduck suffers from relentless headaches. No one is certain if the psychic powers it uses are intentional or if they just get out of control sometimes.

Pyukumuku

Type: Water

Height & Weight:
0.3m/1.2 kg

Pyukumuku coats its body in slippery slime to keep its skin from drying out if it washes up on the beach. Fortunately, Alola's residents have made a tradition out of chucking these Pokémon back into the water when that happens.

Alolan Raichu

Type:
Electric–Psychic

Height & Weight:
0.7 m/21.0 kg

The Alola region is known for its fluffy, delicious pancakes, and Alolan Raichu just loves to eat them. Perhaps there's a connection . . .

Alolan Raticate

Type:
Dark–Normal

Height & Weight:
0.7 m/25.5 kg

Alolan Raticate has a very particular palate and seeks out food of the highest quality, both in taste and in nutrition. It commands a group of Rattata to find the best food.

Alolan Rattata

Type:
Dark–Normal

Height & Weight:
0.3 m/3.8 kg

The impressive moustache that Alolan Rattata sports is made of whiskers that enhance its sense of smell. It can sniff out food and track it down, even if the food is well hidden.

Ribombee

Type: Bug–Fairy

Height & Weight:
0.2 m/0.5 kg

Ribombee's expert weather sense helps it avoid the rain. When the skies have been clear for a while, this Pokémon emerges from its hiding place inside a tree to look for dry pollen.

Riolu

Type: Fighting

Height & Weight:
0.7 m/20.2 kg

Riolu senses the auras of people and Pokémon to determine how they're feeling, and it emits waves of its own aura to silently communicate with its peers while avoiding detection by foes. If it senses an opponent who's much stronger, it stays away.

Rockruff

Type: Rock

Height & Weight:
0.5 m/9.2 kg

Rockruff's love can hurt – it snuggles up to people it likes and rubs its rocky neck ruff against them. Some Trainers welcome this rough affection when Rockruff is small but can't deal with it as the Pokémon grows up.

Rowlet

Type:
Grass–Flying

Height & Weight:
0.3 m/1.5 kg

Rowlet takes comfort from dark, enclosed spaces and sometimes nestles into its Trainer's backpack for a nap. In battle, it flings its sharp-edged feathers and unleashes powerful kicks.

Sableye

Type: Dark–Ghost

Height & Weight:
0.5 m/11.0 kg

Sableye uses its strong claws to dig through the ground in search of gemstones, which it grinds up and eats with its jagged teeth – so Carbink better beware! The patterns on its body vary depending on the composition of the gems it's consumed.

Salandit

Type: Poison–Fire

Height & Weight:
0.6 m/4.8 kg

Because they expend so much energy gathering food for the females who boss them around, male Salandit are unable to evolve. This Pokémon attacks with poison gas that leaves its foes unsteady – well, except for Spinda, who's already quite dizzy.

Salazzle

Type:
Poison–Fire

Height & Weight:
1.2 m/22.2 kg

Salazzle gives off pheromones to attract and recruit Salandit who serve at its beck and call. Those who fail to heed its commands to bring it food are met with a fiery slap.

Sandile

Type: Ground–Dark

Height & Weight:
0.7 m/15.2 kg

A poor hunter who lacks the skills to find its own food, Sandile is often called "the cleaner of the desert" because it scavenges for scraps in the sand. It loves warm places, so it feels at home in Alola, where it can even live outside the desert.

Alolan Sandshrew

Type:
Ice–Steel

**Height &
Weight:**
0.7 m/40.0 kg

The ice that coats Alolan Sandshrew's body allows it to slide across the ground at high speeds. It rockets itself towards opponents to knock them off their feet.

Alolan Sandslash

Type:
Ice–Steel

**Height &
Weight:**
1.2 m/55.0 kg

In Alola's snowy mountains, Alolan Sandslash has developed a protective shield of icy spikes. Its body gives off freezing air that builds up the spikes.

Sandygast

Type:
Ghost–Ground

Height & Weight:
0.5 m/70.0 kg

Children who abandon the piles of sand they built while playing by the water may return to find the beach overrun with Sandygast. If they leave a shovel behind, this Pokémon will fight them for it.

Scizor

Type: Bug–Steel

Height & Weight:
1.8 m/118.0 kg

With a body as hard as steel, Scizor uses its bulky pincers to deliver merciless blows with destructive force. Because the pincers are so durable, they're well suited to this type of attack – grasping at foes just isn't as effective.

Scyther

Type:
Bug–Flying

**Height &
Weight:**
1.5 m/56.0 kg

Scyther conceals itself in tall grass, waiting for the perfect time to spring out and swing its bladed arms at its foe. It moves with the stealth and grace of a ninja.

Seaking

Type:
Water

Height & Weight:
1.3 m/39.0 kg

When it's time to construct a nest, male Seaking use the horn on their heads to hollow out a spot among submerged boulders. For some reason, the females don't participate in this task.

Sharpedo

Type: Water–Dark

Height & Weight: 1.8 m/88.8 kg

Sharpedo takes in seawater through its mouth and releases it from behind in a powerful spout. This action propels it through the water. Sailors and other seafarers can often be seen wearing Sharpedo-fang accessories to ward off bad luck.

Shellder

Type: Water

Height & Weight: 0.3 m/4.0 kg

The solid shell of a Shellder can stand up to any opponent and ward off any attack. When the shell is open, its soft body is vulnerable.

Shiinotic

Type: Grass–Fairy

Height & Weight: 1.0 m/11.5 kg

Shiinotic's touch can be a blessing or a curse. With the tips of its arms, it can heal allies – but it can also drain energy from foes it's lulled to sleep. It spars with Parasect over territory, covering the ground with spores in the process.

Silvally

Type: Normal

Height & Weight: 2.3 m/100.5 kg

Forming a strong bond with its Trainer gave this Pokémon the will to break free of the control mask holding it in check. Without the burden of the heavy mask, Silvally can move much more easily and quickly.

Slowbro

Type: Water–Psychic

Height & Weight: 1.6 m/78.5 kg

Slowbro spends most of its time relaxing near the water's edge. The Shellder on its tail is an integral part of its identity – without Shellder, it's basically just a Slowpoke.

Slowking

Type: Water–Psychic

Height & Weight: 2.0 m/79.5 kg

Slowking is brilliant but absent-minded. It's always thinking up amazing new ideas … and forgetting them in the next moment. Oranguru sometimes challenges it to a battle of wits, but those matches often go unresolved.

Slowpoke

Type: Water–Psychic

Height & Weight: 1.2 m/36.0 kg

Slowpoke definitely lives up to its name – it takes its sweet time getting from one place to another. It would much rather stay put, lounging the day away.

Snorlax

Type: Normal

Height & Weight: 2.1 m/460.0 kg

If you find some expired food in your pantry, there's no need to throw it out! Snorlax will happily scarf it down – its stomach doesn't seem to mind.

Solgaleo

Type: Psychic–Steel

Height & Weight: 3.4 m/230.0 kg

An ancient legend refers to this Pokémon as "the beast that devours the sun". When Solgaleo opens an Ultra Wormhole, strange life-forms from another world sometimes appear.

Spinarak

Type: Bug–Poison

Height & Weight: 0.5 m/8.5 kg

The threads Spinarak uses to spin its web are so sturdy that the web can hold a rock without breaking. Opponents get caught in the web and tire themselves out, helped along by Spinarak's poison.

Stakataka

Type: Rock–Steel

Height & Weight: 5.5 m/820.0 kg

It's thought that Stakataka, one of the mysterious Ultra Beasts, is made up of several lifeforms stacked on top of one another. This creature resembles a stone wall covered with markings that look like blue eyes.

Starmie

Type: Water–Psychic

Height & Weight: 1.1 m/80.0 kg

At the centre of Starmie's body is a core that looks like a gem. The core can glow in seven different colours, and people believe these colours may be communication signals.

Staryu

Type:
Water

Height & Weight:
0.8 m/34.5 kg

Staryu has amazing regenerative powers. If its core remains unscathed, it can heal all of its other body parts following a tough battle.

Steenee

Type: Grass

Height & Weight:
0.7 m/8.2 kg

Shielded by the tough sepals on its head, Steenee cavorts through life with little concern for the Flying-type Pokémon who like to peck at it. When it's bouncing around, its Trainer must stand clear to avoid being struck by the sepals.

Stoutland

Type: Normal

Height & Weight:
1.2 m/61.0 kg

Stoutland's long, dense fur coat protects it from freezing temperatures, so the Alola region can be a bit warm for its taste. Long ago, it was a must-have Pokémon for people living in colder regions.

Stufful

Type: Normal–Fighting

Height & Weight:
0.5 m/6.8 kg

You can look, but don't touch! Otherwise, Stufful will throw a spectacular tantrum with enough destructive power to split a tree in two. It communicates with other Stufful by emitting odours from an organ on its rear.

Sudowoodo

Type: Rock

Height & Weight:
1.2 m/38.0 kg

Because Sudowoodo is always pretending to be a tree, it has to hold its arms up all the time, so its arms have grown very strong. Elderly Trainers have a particular fondness for this Pokémon and read magazines about it.

Sylveon

Type: Fairy

Height & Weight:
1.0 m/23.5 kg

Sylveon stays attuned to its Trainer's mood by grasping their arm with its feelers, which look like flowing ribbons. When faced with a Dragon-type opponent, no matter the size, it leaps into battle with ferocity.

Tapu Bulu

Type: Grass–Fairy

Height & Weight:
1.9 m/45.5 kg

Tapu Bulu prefers to avoid conflict, but if it encounters an enemy, it will attack without question. The end of its tail gives off a ringing sound. It's known as the guardian of Ula'ula Island.

Tapu Fini

Type: Water–Fairy

Height & Weight:
1.3 m/21.2 kg

Tapu Fini shrouds itself in a dense fog, inspiring fear and awe in many. Those who don't take the hint to leave this Pokémon alone sometimes find themselves in dire straits. It's known as the guardian of Poni Island.

Tapu Koko

Type:
Electric–Fairy

Height & Weight:
1.8 m/20.5 kg

Tapu Koko is curious and eager to investigate anything that catches its eye, but if something makes it angry, it lashes out with lightning. It's known as the guardian of Melemele Island.

Tapu Lele

Type:
Psychic–Fairy

Height & Weight:
1.2 m/18.6 kg

Tapu Lele can be kind, showering its shining scales down on people and Pokémon to cure their injuries. It can also be cruel, showing no remorse when it hurts someone. It's known as the guardian of Akala Island.

Tauros

Type:
Normal

Height & Weight:
1.4 m/88.4 kg

Tauros has a rambunctious nature and seemingly endless stamina. When it charges, it just keeps going until it runs into something.

Tentacool

Type:
Water–Poison

Height & Weight:
0.9 m/45.5 kg

If you come across a parched Tentacool on the beach, do it a favour and help it back into the water. It'll be back to fighting shape in no time.

Tentacruel

Type: Water–Poison

Height & Weight: 1.6 m/55.0 kg

Tentacruel overwhelms its opponents by encircling them with its 80 flexible tentacles. The tentacles secrete a toxin that drains the energy of whoever's unlucky enough to be in their grasp.

Togedemaru

Type: Electric–Steel

Height & Weight: 0.3 m/3.3 kg

Togedemaru can't produce much electricity on its own, so it gets hit by lightning on purpose to power itself up. About a dozen spikes made of fur stand straight up on its back when this Pokémon is distressed.

Torracat

Type: Fire

Height & Weight: 0.7 m/25.0 kg

If Torracat's mane is lying sleek and flat, it might be in poor health or a bad mood – the mane bristles up magnificently when it's feeling fine. Its Trainer often bears the marks of its sharp claws.

Toucannon

Type: Normal–Flying

Height & Weight: 1.1 m/26.0 kg

Because Toucannon live happily in pairs with little squabbling, people sometimes bring them to weddings in Alola as inspiration to the newlyweds. A clash of beaks is a conversation, not a duel.

Toxapex

Type: Poison–Water

Height & Weight: 0.7 m/14.5 kg

Toxapex can attack at range by flinging toxic spikes or claw with its legs when battling up close. It can also curl its legs around itself to form a dome-shaped shield for protection from the tide.

Trubbish

Type: Poison

Height & Weight: 0.6 m/31.0 kg

Trubbish exhales a foul-smelling, poisonous gas that can be very dangerous to children and smaller Pokémon. Muk flock to this stench in hopes of finding something tasty to eat.

Trumbeak

Type: Normal–Flying

Height & Weight: 0.6 m/14.8 kg

After Trumbeak eats berries, it stores the seeds in its beak and fires them at opponents. After a battle, some of the seeds take root and grow more berries. Its flexible beak produces many different sounds.

Tsareena

Type: Grass

Height & Weight: 1.2 m/21.4 kg

A graceful yet fierce Pokémon, Tsareena is known for its impressive kicks that can knock down even the most experienced fighters. It seems to delight in its own skills, laughing as it pummels its opponents.

Turtonator

Type: Fire–Dragon

Height & Weight: 2.0 m/212.0 kg

Turtonator makes its home in a volcano, where it eats minerals like sulphur. Those minerals combine inside its body to form the explosive spikes on its shell. Getting them wet is a bad idea, so Turtonator hides from the rain.

Type: Null

Type: Normal

Height & Weight: 1.9 m/120.5 kg

The synthetic Pokémon known as Type: Null wears a heavy mask to keep its power in check. It once went on a rampage when scientists were conducting an experiment, so now they don't take any chances.

Umbreon

Type: Dark

Height & Weight: 1.0 m/27.0 kg

When Umbreon pounces on an opponent, the yellow ring markings in its fur give off an ominous glow. Its large eyes are well adapted for battle in complete darkness.

Vaporeon

Type: Water

Height & Weight: 1.0 m/29.0 kg

The structure of Vaporeon's cells closely resembles the structure of a water molecule. Because of this similarity, this Pokémon is almost invisible when it moves through the water.

Vikavolt

Type: Bug–Electric

Height & Weight:
1.5 m/45.0 kg

Vikavolt uses its large jaws to focus the electricity it produces inside its body, then unleashes a powerful zap to stun its opponents. It's quite the acrobat in the air, confounding its opponents with skilful flying.

Alolan Vulpix

Type:
Ice

Height & Weight:
0.6 m/9.9 kg

Alolan Vulpix, also known as Keokeo, is covered in fluffy white fur that offers camouflage in its snowy habitat. It blows frosty air from its mouth.

Wailmer

Type: Water

Height & Weight:
2.0 m/130.0 kg

Distant memories of life on the land occasionally cause groups of Wailmer to wash up on shore. As this Pokémon swims, it takes in large quantities of seawater, then surfaces to spray that water out of its nostrils.

Wailord

Type: Water

Height & Weight:
14.5 m/398.0 kg

Big groups of Wailord can cause an imbalance in their environment because they require so much food. A Dhelmise or Sharpedo who goes after a Wailmer might find itself facing down an enormous pod of Wailord.

Wigglytuff

Type:
Normal–Fairy

Height & Weight:
1.0 m/12.0 kg

Wigglytuff's body is incredibly flexible and can expand just like a balloon. It takes deep breaths, puffing itself up with air so it appears larger.

Wimpod

Type: Bug–Water

Height & Weight:
0.5 m/12.0 kg

Although it's terrified of just about everything and speeds away at the first sign of trouble, Wimpod has a weakness for objects it finds on the ground. If it happens to find a coin, it risks unwanted attention from Murkrow or Meowth.

Wingull

Type: Water–Flying

Height & Weight:
0.6 m/9.5 kg

After taking off from its cliffside nest, Wingull soars like a glider above the sea as it searches for food hidden underwater. Its slender wings are an ideal size and shape for catching the wind.

Wishiwashi
(Solo Form)

Type:
Water

Height & Weight:
8.2 m/78.6 kg

When many Wishiwashi come together in a school to take on a stronger opponent, they become so powerful that their School Form is known as the "demon of the sea".

Wishiwashi
(School Form)

Type: Water

Height & Weight:
0.2 m/0.3 kg

A single Wishiwashi isn't a very formidable opponent, so they usually travel in schools. When a Wishiwashi is in trouble, its eyes give off a light that can be seen from a distance to attract the rest of its school.

Wobbuffet

Type:
Psychic

Height & Weight:
1.3 m/28.5 kg

Relying on its powers of endurance, Wobbuffet prefers not to attack – unless a foe goes after its tail. Then, it unleashes a powerful counterstrike.

Xurkitree
Ultra Beast

Type: Electric

Height & Weight:
3.8 m/100.0 kg

A strange and mysterious Ultra Beast, Xurkitree can sometimes be found motionless, with its limbs firmly planted into the ground like a tree. It's apparently a common sight on its home world, even though it poses a threat to this one.

Zubat

Type:
Poison–Flying

Height & Weight:
0.8 m/7.5 kg

Zubat monitors its surroundings by bouncing ultrasonic waves off nearby objects. This skill helps it avoid mid-air collisions while flying.

Pick a Path

Begin at the START, then move one Poké Ball (down, sideways or diagonally) at a time to reach the FINISH. Only real Poké Balls will show you the true path.

START

KNOT	IRON	ELEC	DUSK
LAST	DAWN	FIELD	REPEAT
CRYSTAL	QUICK	NEST	FOOT
MASTER	FLAME	STONE	AIR
BLITZ	ULTRA	FREE	WET

FINISH

The answers are on page 69.

The Professor's Quiz

Professor Kukui has set his students a quiz all about the Pokémon and Ultra Beasts that can be found in the Alola region. How well are your own studies going? Take the quiz to find out!

1 Which of these Pokémon does not have a separate Alolan form?

A. Persian ☐   **B.** Raticate ☐   **C.** Stufful ☐

Use the Alolan A–Z pages if you get stuck.

2 What type of Pokémon is Meltan?

A. Ghost ☐   **B.** Dark ☐   **C.** Steel ☐

3 Is Kartana a Legendary Pokémon or an Ultra Beast?

A. Legendary ☐   **B.** Ultra Beast ☐

4 Gyarados is the final Evolution form of which Water-type Pokémon?

A. Luvdisc ☐   **B.** Magikarp ☐   **C.** Seaking ☐

5 Lycanroc can evolve from Rockruff into how many different forms?

A. two ☐   **B.** three ☐   **C.** four ☐

6 Which Normal-type baby Pokémon eats almost anything that's edible?

A. Pichu ☐   **B.** Munchlax ☐   **C.** Igglybuff ☐

7 Which Electric-type Pokémon is Sophocles' trusted friend?

A. Electabuzz ☐   **B.** Pikachu ☐   **C.** Togedemaru ☐

8 Name the Water-type Pokémon that exists in Solo Form and School Form.

A. Popplio ☐   **B.** Wishiwashi ☐   **C.** Remoraid ☐

The answers are on page 69.

Double Take

Ash and his friends from the Pokémon School have come face to face with a Legendary Pokémon! There are eight differences in the second picture. Can you find them all?

The answers are on page 69.

In Line

Study these Pokémon patterns, then write the name of the Pokémon that is missing from each row. Expert Trainers could try drawing the Pokémon, too!

1 Clefable Drowzee Clefable Drowzee Clefable Drowzee Clefable ....

2 Alolan Diglett Fomantis Alolan Geodude .... Fomantis Alolan Geodude

3 Alolan Muk Alolan Muk Alolan Muk Nosepass .... Nosepass

4 Parasect Alolan Raticate Sableye Parasect Alolan Raticate ....

5 Magikarp Magikarp .... Magikarp Magikarp Misdreavus

The answers are on page 69.

Who's Hungry?

Colour in the shapes with a dot to reveal which pair of Pokémon has earned a tasty treat.

The answers are on page 69.

Answers

Pages 8-9
Rotom Reboot
1. Alolan Meowth; 2. Komala;
3. Goldeen; 4. Bounsweet; 5. Sableye;
6. Litten; 7. Stoutland; 8. Clefable

Pages 10-11
Prepare for Battle
Ash vs Jessie
PIKACHU vs MEOWTH
INCINEROAR vs MIMIKYU
LYCANROC (Dusk form) vs SABLEYE.

Ash vs James
MELTAN vs BEWEAR
NAGANADEL vs MAREANIE
ROWLET vs WOBBUFFET.

Page 12
Scavenger Hunt
There are 23 Alolan Rattata.
Alolan Rattata is Dark–Normal type.

Page 13
Snowy Search

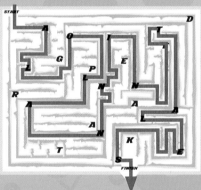

Evolved form = ALOLAN NINETALES.

Page 14
Watery Wonder
B, D, A, F, E, C

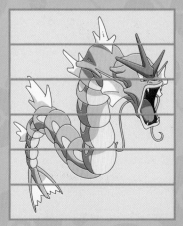

Page 15
Having a Blast
The Pokémon is Turtonator.

Page 26
Ultra Test

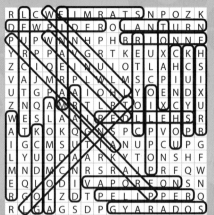

Page 46
Pick a Path

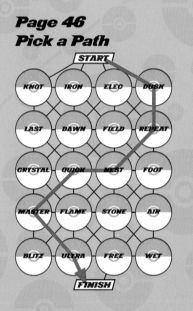

Page 47
The Professor's Quiz
1. C – Stufful; 2. C – Steel;
3. B – Ultra Beast; 4. B – Magikarp;
5. B – three; 6. B – Munchlax;
7. C – Togedemaru; 8. B – Wishiwashi.

Page 48
Double Take

Page 58
Gone Fishing

Page 59
Mystery Memo
The message reads: A DANGEROUS
ULTRA BEAST HAS BEEN DISCOVERED
ON PONI ISLAND. NAMED GUZZLORD,
IT CAN SWALLOW BUILDINGS AND
MOUNTAINS WHOLE.

Pages 60-61
Park Quest
The coordinates are:
1. B3; 2. E1; 3. A4 & A5; 4. E4; 5. B6;
6. G3; 7. F2; 8. A3; 9. C4; 10. D1; 11. F7.

Page 62
Rocket Robbery
The Z-Ring was taken by Jessie.

Page 65
Crossing Paths

Page 67
In Line
1. Drowzee; 2. Alolan Diglett;
3. Nosepass; 4. Sableye; 5. Misdreavus.

Page 68
Who's Hungry?
The Pokémon are Munchlax
and Pikachu.